RACING
through the
ALPHABET

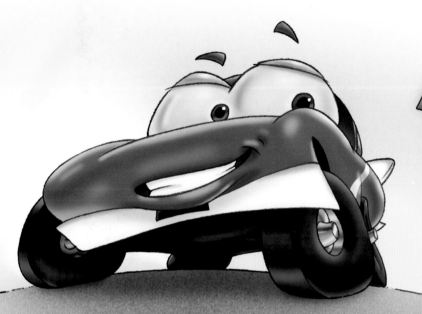

Axel Alphabet and his story
Racing Through the Alphabet
were inspired by an idea by

CAMERON &
TAYLOR PRUETT

To God above for giving us so many blessings,
and to our dearest race fans, Lauren, Taylor and Cameron.

Summary: Learning your alphabet has never been so much fun! Race along with Axel Alphabet as he
shares his favorite letters and racing words from A to Z. First printing 2008.

ISBN 0-9670600-3-6

Racing through the Alphabet / by Scott and Judy Pruett
Design and Art Direction / by Glen Eytchison
Illustration / by Rick Morgan

Special thanks to our "art guy" Glen Eytchison for his dedication and effort to continually get it "just
right"; our illustrator Rick Morgan for his special humor and always reminding us "it's a cartoon"; and
to Mike Dietz, for always being there when we need him.

I'm racing through the alphabet, won't you come along with me?

I'll show you all the lefts and rights from A to Z.

We'll take a lap around the track, we'll have some fun and then

Once we cross the finish line we can do it all again!

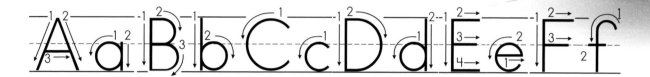

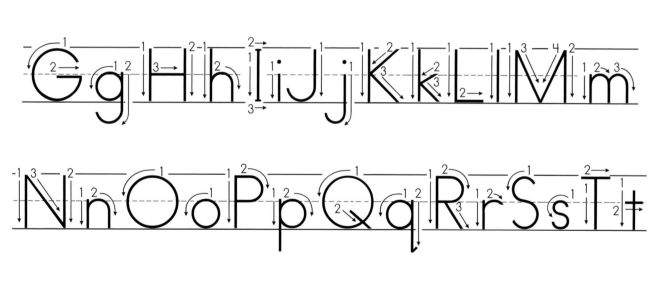

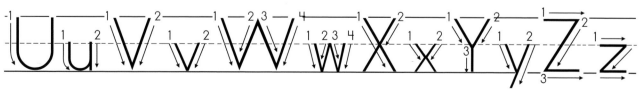

A is for announcers, if you're at home or at the track.
They tell you what's going on in the race, from the front straight to the back.

AaBbCcDdEeFfGgHhIiJjKkLlMmNnOoPpQqRrSsTtUuVvWwXxYyZz

Bb

B is for brakes I need, because I'm going really fast.
When I'm coming up on one of those turns I don't want to go straight past!

AaBbCcDdEeFfGgHhIiJjKkLlMmNnOoPpQqRrSsTtUuVvWwXxYyZz

Cc

C is for crew guys, without them there's no race.
They do my pit stops really fast, and help me get first place.

A a B b **C c** D d E e F f G g H h I i J j K k L l M m N n O o P p Q q R r S s T t U u V v W w X x Y y Z z

Dd

D is for driver, he helps steer and brake and chase.
We work together as a team to try and win the race.

AaBbCc**Dd**EeFfGgHhIiJjKkLlMmNnOoPpQqRrSsTtUuVvWwXxYyZz

Ee

E is for engine, it sits underneath my hood.
It starts up with a giant roar that sounds and feels so good.

AaBbCcDdEeFfGgHhIiJjKkLlMmNnOoPpQqRrSsTtUuVvWwXxYyZz

F is for fans like you that cheer me on as I go.
I love to hear you scream and shout more than you could ever know.

AaBbCcDdEe**Ff**GgHhIiJjKkLlMmNnOoPpQqRrSsTtUuVvWwXxYyZz

Gg

G is for grid where we line up side by side.
In the order that we qualified, we take our place with pride.

AaBbCcDdEeFf **Gg** HhIiJjKkLlMmNnOoPpQqRrSsTtUuVvWwXxYyZz

Hh

H is for hauler, the big trucks that you see.
My Hauler's name is Harry, he takes good care of me.

AaBbCcDdEeFfGg**Hh**IiJjKkLlMmNnOoPpQqRrSsTtUuVvWwXxYyZz

Ii

I is for inspections, done to keep things fair.
Until you pass inspection, you can't go anywhere.

AaBbCcDdEeFfGgHhIiJjKkLlMmNnOoPpQqRrSsTtUuVvWwXxYyZz

Jj

J is for jackman, his job takes strength and speed.
He lifts me up for the crew to put on the tires that I need.

AaBbCcDdEeFfGgHhIiJjKkLlMmNnOoPpQqRrSsTtUuVvWwXxYyZz

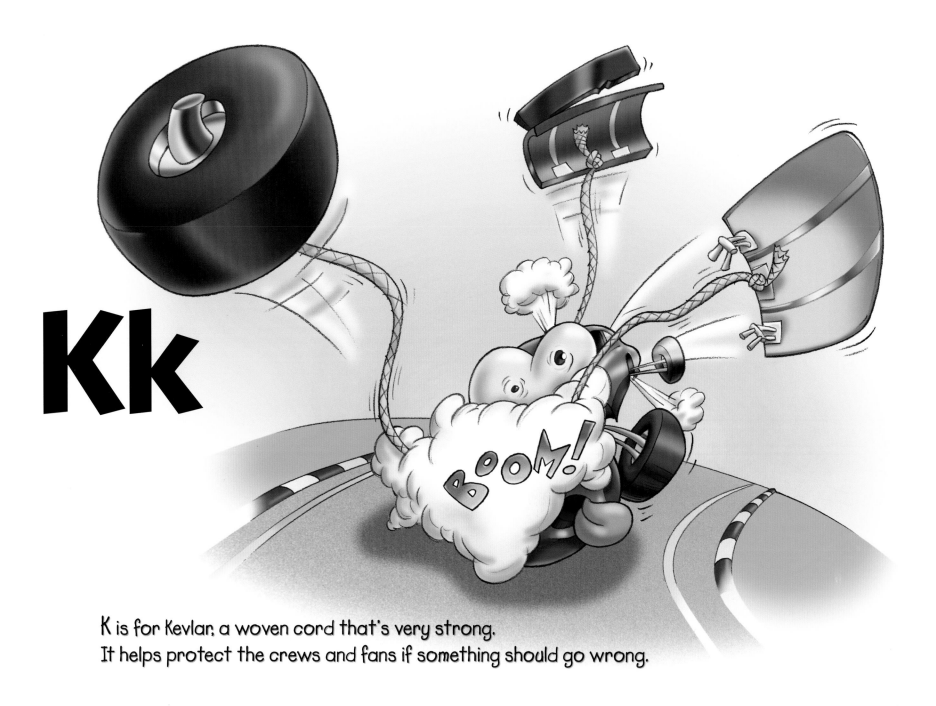

Kk

K is for Kevlar, a woven cord that's very strong.
It helps protect the crews and fans if something should go wrong.

AaBbCcDdEeFfGgHhIiJj**Kk**LlMmNnOoPpQqRrSsTtUuVvWwXxYyZz

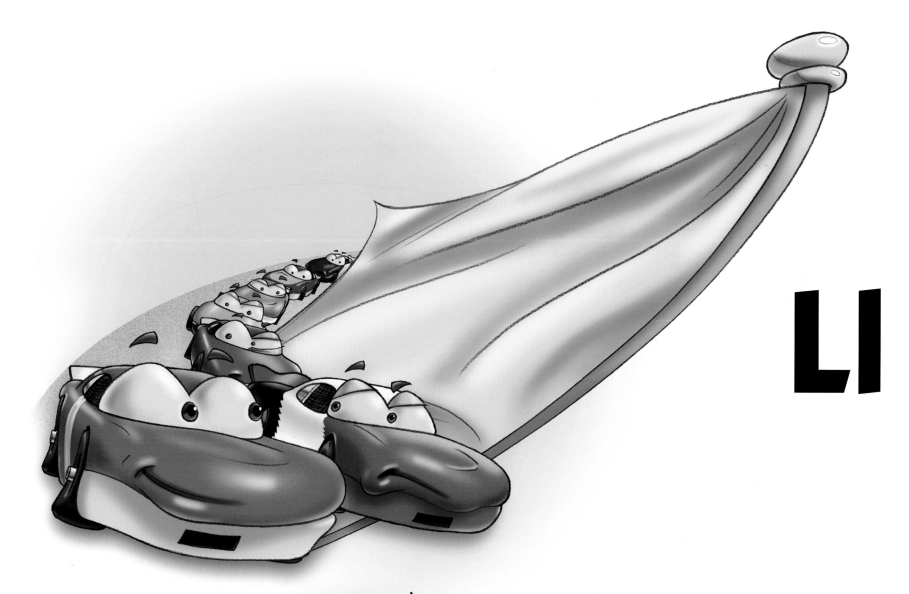

Ll

L is for lucky dog, the first racecar one lap down.
When the yellow's out, he passes the leader and goes all the way around.

AaBbCcDdEeFfGgHhIiJjKk**Ll**MmNnOoPpQqRrSsTtUuVvWwXxYyZz

Mm

M is for mechanic, there are many on my team.
They're the ones that turn the nuts and bolts, the best you've ever seen.

AaBbCcDdEeFfGgHhIiJjKkLl**Mm**NnOoPpQqRrSsTtUuVvWwXxYyZz

Nn

N is for Nomex, the fireproof cloth in the driver's suits.
It's used for the head sock and underwear, right down to the fireproof boots.

AaBbCcDdEeFfGgHhIiJjKkLlMm**Nn**OoPpQqRrSsTtUuVvWwXxYyZz

O is for officials, they do many jobs with care.
On the track and in the pits, they make sure the race is fair.

Pp

P is for pit stop, when my crew chief calls me in.
I hit my mark for fuel and tires and then I'm off again.

A a B b C c D d E e F f G g H h I i J j K k L l M m N n O o **P p** Q q R r S s T t U u V v W w X x Y y Z z

Qq

Q is for qualify, a scary thing we all must do.
It determines where we'll start the race, the crew is counting on you.

AaBbCcDdEeFfGgHhIiJjKkLlMmNnOoPp**Qq**RrSsTtUuVvWwXxYyZz

Rr

R is for Rookie Racer, his first year on the track.
You can tell that he's a rookie by the yellow stripe on his back.

AaBbCcDdEeFfGgHhIiJjKkLlMmNnOoPpQqRrSsTtUuVvWwXxYyZz

Ss

S is for sponsors, they help me live the dream.
It takes a lot of money to run a good race team.

AaBbCcDdEeFfGgHhIiJjKkLlMmNnOoPpQqRr**Ss**TtUuVvWwXxYyZz

Tt

T is for tires, the rubber hoops I need.
We call the new ones stickers, and they give me more speed.

Uu

U is for underdog, the little car that could.
He never gives up, always does his best, like every racer should.

V is for vendors, they sell shirts, souvenirs and snacks.
Your favorite driver on the front and racecar on the back.

W is for white flag, one lap left to run.
Racing hard, wheel-to-wheel, it's time to get it done.

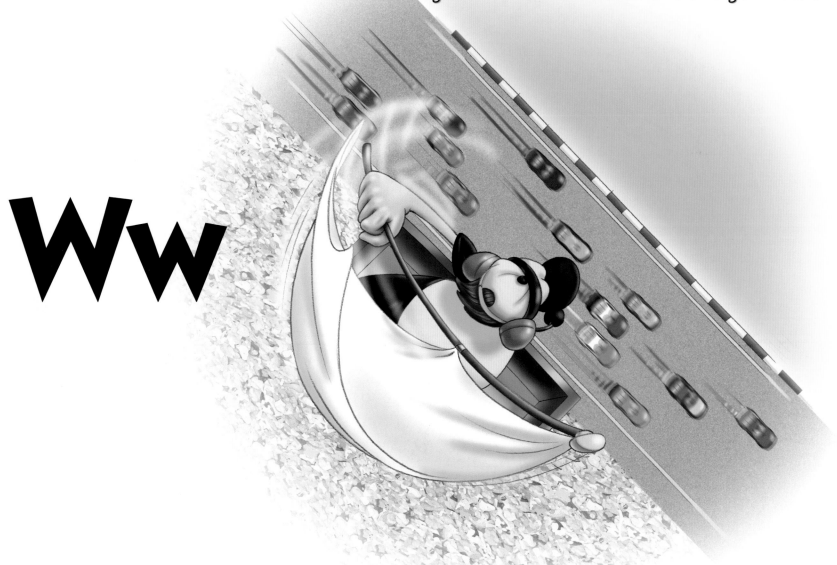

Ww

A a B b C c D d E e F f G g H h I i J j K k L l M m N n O o P p Q q R r S s T t U u V v **W** w X x Y y Z z

X is for X marks the spot, the team marks it in the pit.
When I come in for my pit stop, it's the place that I must hit.

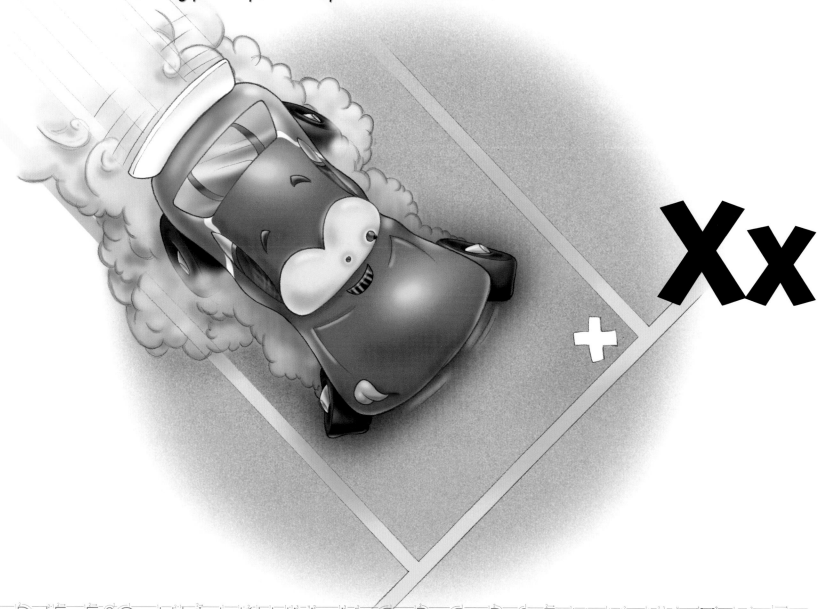

AaBbCcDdEeFfGgHhIiJjKkLlMmNnOoPpQqRrSsTtUuVvWwXxYyZz

Yy

Y is for yellow flag, it means trouble on the track.
We all slow down, the pace car rolls and bunches up the pack.

AaBbCcDdEeFfGgHhIiJjKkLlMmNnOoPpQqRrSsTtUuVvWwXxYyZz

Zz

Z is for zoom, it means going really fast.
Z is my favorite letter too, I just can't believe it's LAST!!!

AaBbCcDdEeFfGgHhIiJjKkLlMmNnOoPpQqRrSsTtUuVvWwXxYyZz

Twelve Little Race Cars, Twelve More Little Race Cars and Rookie Racer
are hardcover, 32 pages, illustrated in full color, and priced at $12.95 (USD) each.

To order, print and complete this form and mail it along with your payment to:
Word Weaver Books, Inc., 9743 West Bray Creek St. Star, ID 83669

Name: _____ Phone: _____

Address: _____

City: _____ State: _____ Zip: _____

Shipping:
(1-2 Books $6.00)
(3-4 Books $9.00)
(5-6 Books $12.00)

Sales Tax: If ordering from within the state of Nevada, please add 7.5% of total

Twelve Little Race Cars ($12.95 per book)

Quantity Ordered _____ Subtotal _____

Twelve More Little Race Cars ($12.95 per book)

Quantity Ordered _____ Subtotal _____

Rookie Racer ($12.95 per book)

Quantity Ordered _____ Subtotal _____

Racing Through the Alphabet ($12.95 per book)

Quantity Ordered _____ Subtotal _____

Sales Tax .... _____

Shipping .... _____

Total .... _____

Check or money order only; please print clearly; allow 4-6 weeks for delivery.

About the Authors

Scott and Judy Pruett live with their three children Lauren, Taylor and Cameron in Auburn, California.

Scott and Judy Pruett live with their three children Lauren, Taylor and Cameron in Auburn, California. In 1999, Scott and Judy formed Word Weaver Books to bring their love of racing to the world of children's publishing. "Racing Through The Alphabet" is the fourth of, what they hope to be, many books to come. For more information visit their web site at www.wordweaverbooks.com.

Scott, a renowned professional race car driver and seven time Champion, began his career racing Go-Karts at the age eight. Through hard work and determination he worked his way up the "racing ladder" winning numerous professional and non-professional titles, including: 1986 and 1988 IMSA Champion; 1987, 1994, and 2003 Trans Am Champion; 2004 Grand American Rolex Series Champion, and 1989 Indy 500 Rookie of the Year. He raced ten years in the C.A.R.T. Series (formerly known as Indy Cars), achieving three victories, seven poles and numerous podium finishes. He was very instrumental in Firestone's return to, and success in, racing; logging in more than 100,000 miles of testing in 1994. In 1995 Scott earned the first win upon their return, winning the Michigan 500. Scott completed his first full season in the NASCAR Winston (now Sprint) Cup Series driving the #32 Tide car in 2000, and continues to compete in the road courses in that series. Scott has also competed in the IROC (International Race of Champions) series many times, and in 2005 voted, "IROC Legend" in the road racing category. He is currently competing in the Rolex Grand American Series driving the #01 Telmex Chip Ganassi Racing car. He won the Championship in 2004 and has scored prestigious back-to-back wins in the Rolex 24 Hours of Daytona in 2007 and 2008. Beyond racing Scott is a devoted husband and father and enjoys wine making at his vineyard, landscape design and working with the earth.

Judy "retired" from the field of Occupational Therapy after enjoying fifteen years of a wonderfully diverse career including work in child development, neurological disorders, spinal cord injuries, sports medicine and upper extremity trauma. She is very active with the writing and publishing of their books and strives (like all Moms) to balance her desire to write and promote their books with being involved at school and raising their three beautiful children. Judy also enjoys music, theatre, training with Scott and traveling with him when possible. She counts her blessings daily.

Glen Eytchison has over 30 years of expertise in the related fields of theater, music, fine arts, film and graphic design, including a 17-year tenure as producer/director of the internationally acclaimed Laguna Beach, CA Pageant of the Masters. Gaining recognition for his sophisticated and emotionally compelling designs, his work on Broadway and in regional theater led to design work in advertising, television and feature films, including Warner Bros. releases Devil's Advocate, Wild Wild West, and Columbia's Ghostbusters II. Glen's company, The Eytchison Group, provides design, marketing and new media services to companies like Ford Motor Co., Comedy Central and Walt Disney Entertainment. Glen has been working with Scott and Judy since 1996. He has designed and produced all of the Twelve Little Race Cars books, and currently has several new Twelve Little Race Cars projects in production. (www.eytchisongroup.com)

Rick Morgan has been an illustrator and graphic designer for over 25 years. He is Head Art Guy at the World Headquarters of R morgan illustration & design, and lives in Dana Point, CA, with his lovely wife Tracy, his first dog, Hobie, and a less-than-pleasant cat named Pig. Rick is an inveterate collector of many wonderful, weird and (some would say) worthless things like flags, toy soldiers and hats. Racing Through the Alphabet is the fourth book he has illustrated, either all or in part, for the Pruetts and Glen Eytchison.